Lil Legends

Uppercase Tracing & Vocabulary Book

Writing Practice for Kids

Level 2

India's First Pre-Writing Program

OSWAAL BOOKS®
LEARNING MADE SIMPLE

Lil Legends

An imprint of Oswaal Books & Learning Pvt. Ltd.

PUBLISHED BY

OSWAAL BOOKS & LEARNING PVT. LTD.

INDIA OFFICE
1/11, Sahitya Kunj, M.G. Road,
Agra - 282002, (UP) India

UK OFFICE
1010, Cambourne
Cambridge, Cambridgeshire
CB 23#6DP, United Kingdom

Phone: 0562-2857671
E-mail: contact@oswaalbooks.com
Website: www.Oswaalbooks.com
ISBN: **9789357287067**
Printed at: **Paras Offset Pvt. Ltd., Kundli-131028**

Uppercase Tracing & Vocabulary Book

Writing Practice for Kids

This Book Belongs to

....

Attention Parents...

Introducing India's first Pre-writing Program

Our proprietary writing program, is designed to help toddlers master their pre-writing skills. The program is based on five S-philosophies:

1. Skill Escalation:

All tracing opportunities advance in skill gradually, requiring one to follow the guide in its natural sequence. In this guide, the child will start with practicing the letter tracing in the medium size, progress to small size tracing on four lines and then advance to writing based on smart dots.

2. Strategic Sequence:

The program does not follow the traditional sequence of A, B, C but introduces tracing of alphabets in a strategic way that is best suited to the child's increasing skills and confidence. Letters with straight lines will come first, then letters with slanting lines and finally with curved lines. For example, Letter L will be introduced before A.

3. Smart Dot Guidance:

All patterns have smart guiding dots that are indicators on where to start, where to trace to and when one must lift off their writing instrument. Initially, all smart dots are numbered and coloured. As the guide advances, the child has to trace without trace lines and only with the smart dots. The smart dots in their final stage will not include numbers.

Starting Point: • (Green Dot)

End Point: • (Red Dot)

4. Stimulation based Practice:

The guide allows children to continue to boost their vocabulary by introducing them to over 260+ new words in addition to the 300+ words introduced in level 1.

5. Self- Appreciation:

The guide awards children with a certification to celebrate their learning and their enhanced writing skills.

Writing is an important tool, that must be introduced with great care and responsibility.
This guided pre-writing series is India's first pre-writing program that will allow parents and schools to simplify writing for their children and making pre-writing more structured, effective and fun. The program is aimed to help millions of toddlers to successfully yet responsibly embark on their writing journey.

Our goal in this series is to help parents:

- Learn about the age-appropriate grip goals for children
- Identify grip-appropriate writing instruments for children
- Embark on your child's writing journey in a structured and guided manner
- Simplify learning

Before we start on our child's writing journey, it is important that as parents and educators we are informed about some key developmental milestones.

What is a Pincer Grip? Why Do I need to know about it?

Pincer Grip is a grip between the index finger or middle finger and the thumb to grasp an object. Children are not born with this grip developed and first signs of development start around 9-10 months and this grip is fully developed around the age of 5-6 years.

TYPICAL PENCIL GRASP
DEVELOPMENT FOR HANDWRITING

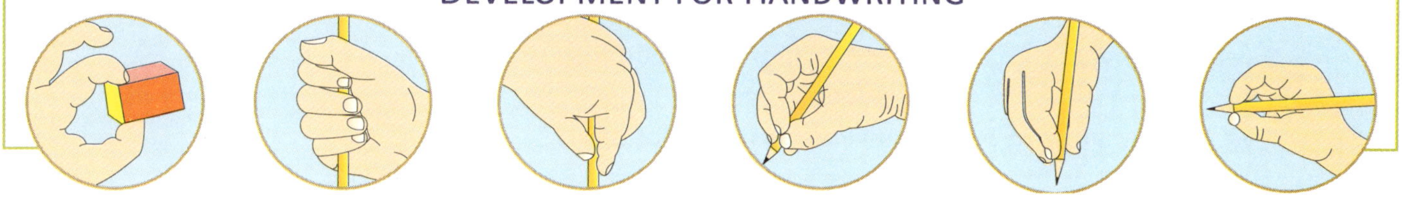

10 Months Pincer Grasp | 12-15 Months Palmar Supinate Grasp | 2-3 Years Digital Pronate Grasp | 3-4 Years Quadrupod Grasp | 3-4 Years Static Tripod Grasp | 5-6 Years Dynamic Tripod Grasp

What happens if a child is made to write before the grip is fully developed?

- Child may develop low self esteem and confidence incase unable to cope with writing.
- Child may become reluctant and unmotivated towards their learning.
- Child may adopt a poor handwriting.
- Child is often misdiagnosed with learning disorders, such as dysgraphia, dyslexia, due to their inability to cope with the existing writing programs, underdeveloped visual-motor skills.
- Causes muscle strain and potential loss of muscle dexterity.

Suggested activities to improve pincer grip development

- Pick and sort objects
- Tearing waste paper
- Pinching bubble wrap, clay, edible dough
- Lacing activities
- Squishing pomegranate, grapes and similar food items
- Open scribbling & mark making
- Colouring on vertical panel

"Before we ever put a pencil in a child's hands, those hands should dig, climb, press, push, squish, twist, and pinch in a wide array of environments and with a variety of materials."

Dr. Amanda Morgan, a world renowned early child expert.

Writing Instrument Guidelines

While their grips are still under development, children can participate in early writing by choosing the correct writing instruments:

- 10 months - 14 months: Ball Crayons (110 mm) & Jumbo Egg Chalk
- 15 months - 20 months: Grasp Crayons (33 mm), Fat Chalk, Dot Markers
- 21 months - 30 months: Grip Crayons (21 mm), Dot Markers, Golf Pencils With Triangular Grips
- 2.5 years - 3.5 years: Thick Crayons (11 mm), Golf Pencils With Grips
- 3.5 years - 4.5 years: Triangular or Hexagonal Pencils with Grip
- 4.5 years: Triangular or Hexagonal Pencils (Grip Optional)

Note: The listed width measurements of the recommended writing instruments are based after studying the effectiveness of the writing tools available for children.

You have picked Level 2: Uppercase Tracing & Vocabulary Book

This guide is focused on helping children master line making.

(1) Children are strategically introduced to tracing letters on four lines.

(2) Children gradually get the opportunity to transit from tracing to writing with only smart dot guidance.

(3) Children continue to expand their vocabulary by learning 260+ new words.

(4) Letters of a similar line construct are sectioned together.

Author Profile

Sonia Agarwal Bajaj

Sonia Agarwal Bajaj is a visionary new age edupreneur, who is making a profound impact in the field of education and skilling.

Sonia's passion to shape young hearts led her to start, Little Chipper International, an experiential learning based preschool in Agra. In a short span of time, this preschool has won many accolades and has been recognized amongst the top 5 Future Ready Preschools in India.

Committed to raising awareness about the importance of early education and helping parents embrace new learning and parenting techniques, Sonia hosts a spectrum of workshops across India. Her newest initiative includes conceptualising and authoring India's first structured pre-writing program for young children.

In addition to her contributions to the space in Early Education, she is the co-founder of Whiz league, an online skilling platform that offers celebrity led masterclasses at affordable prices. With over 1.2 million learning sessions, the platform grew to create its own learning management system that potentially helped hospitality and retail organizations train over 1 Lac staff members on a pan India basis. Sonia led the curriculum design and production for each of the 20 programs listed on the platform.

A Dhirubhai Ambani International School and Babson College alumnae, she has previously held a foray of responsibilities in the space of Ed-tech and fashion retail. Sonia has always been an advocate for the environment and she was a globally recognized founder of Whitenife, a platform that was dedicated to raising awareness on sustainable and ethical fashion.

With deep insight into the process and psychology of learning, Sonia is committed to further transform the education industry in times to come.

LADDER

LIPSTICK

LEGO

LEASH

LADYBUG

LAKE

LET'S PRACTICE TO TRACE LETTER L AND RECOGNISE THESE ASSOCIATED OBJECTS.

NOW, IT'S TIME TO TRACE LETTER L ON THE FOUR LINES.

BRAVO! NOW ONLY FOLLOW THE SMART DOTS TO WRITE THE LETTER L.

LOG

LANTERN

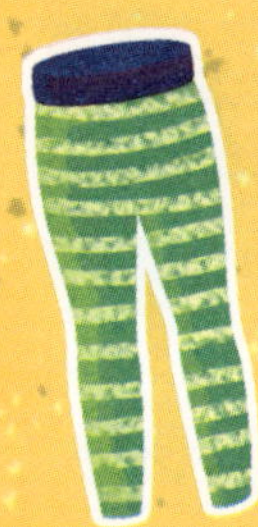

LEGGINGS

LOBSTER

LIBRARY

LILY

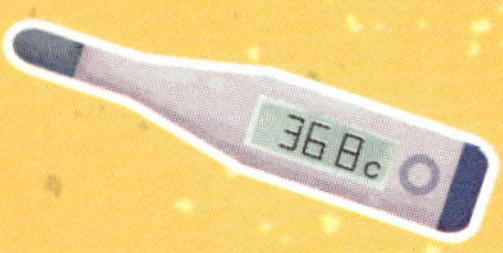

THERMOMETER

TOWEL

TURKEY

T-REX

TELESCOPE

TUNA

LET'S PRACTICE TO TRACE LETTER T AND RECOGNISE THESE ASSOCIATED OBJECTS.

NOW, IT'S TIME TO TRACE LETTER T ON THE FOUR LINES.

BRAVO! NOW ONLY FOLLOW THE SMART DOTS TO WRITE THE LETTER T.

THAILAND

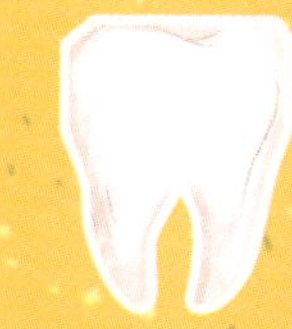

TOOTH

TEAPOT

TELEPHONE

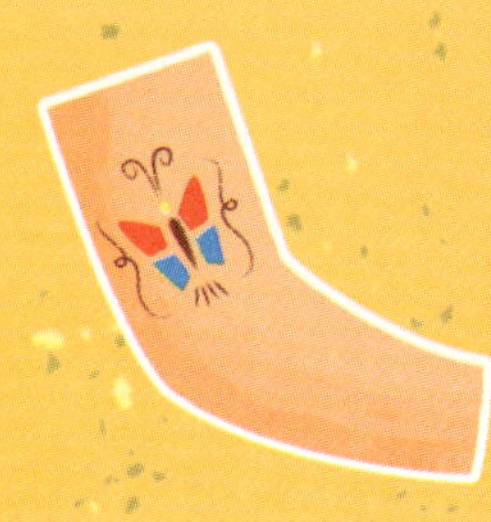

TATTOO

TOAST

ID CARD

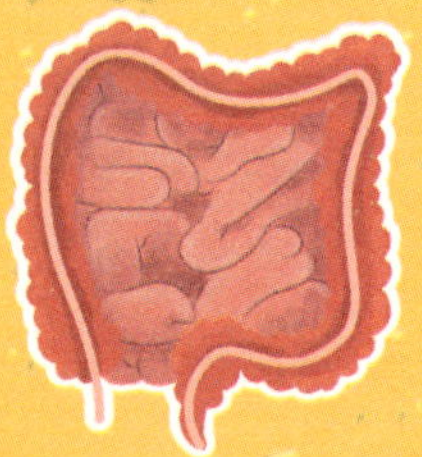

INTESTINE

IMPALA

ISLAND

IVY

ICING

LET'S PRACTICE TO TRACE LETTER I AND RECOGNISE THESE ASSOCIATED OBJECTS.

NOW, IT'S TIME TO TRACE LETTER I ON THE FOUR LINES.

BRAVO! NOW ONLY FOLLOW THE SMART DOTS TO WRITE THE LETTER I.

ICEBERG

IRON BOARD

INCENSE STICK

INHALER

ICE SKATING

INCH TAPE

E-MAIL

EUROPE

EMU

EEL

ESKIMO

EMOTIONS

LET'S PRACTICE TO TRACE LETTER E AND RECOGNISE THESE ASSOCIATED OBJECTS.

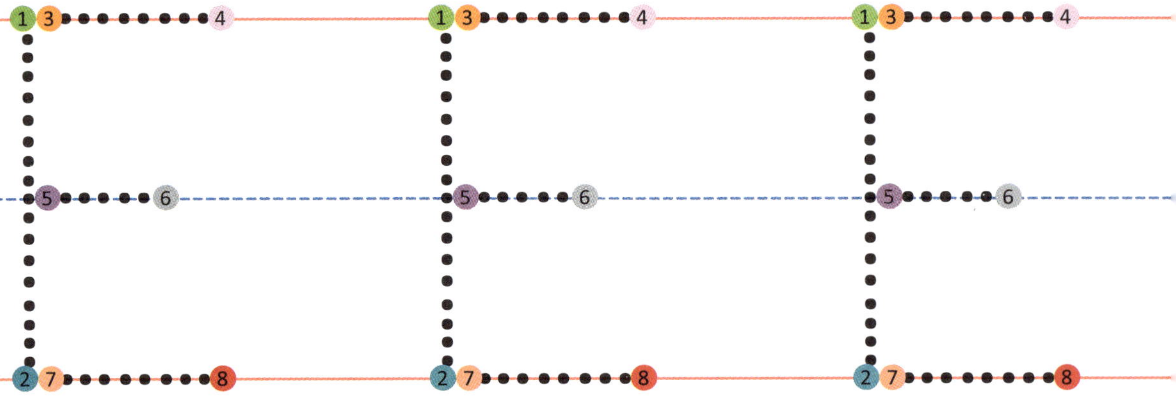

NOW, IT'S TIME TO TRACE LETTER E ON THE FOUR LINES.

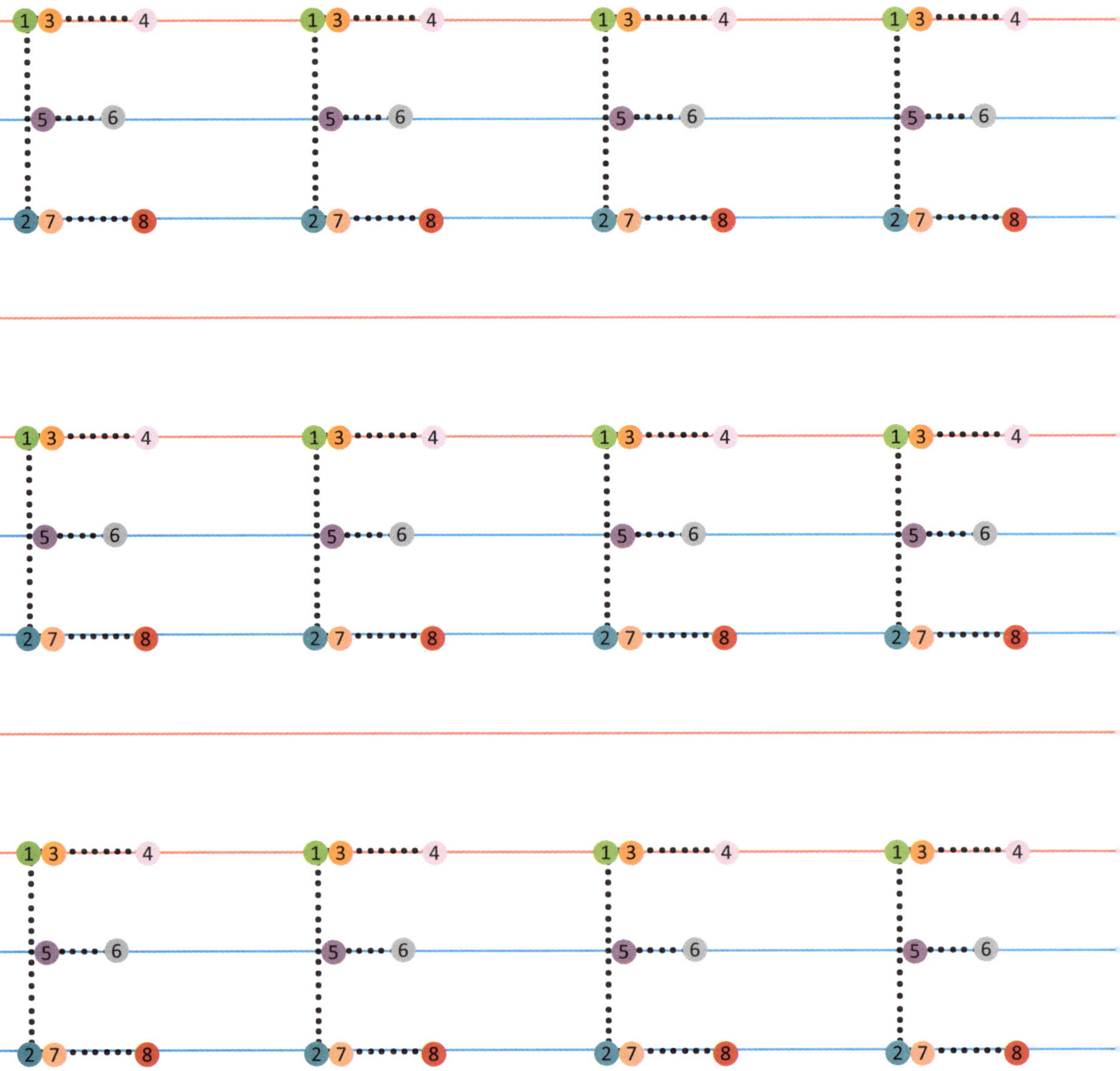

BRAVO! NOW ONLY FOLLOW THE SMART DOTS TO WRITE THE LETTER E.

EASEL

EMERALD

ESCALATOR

EARRINGS

ELBOW

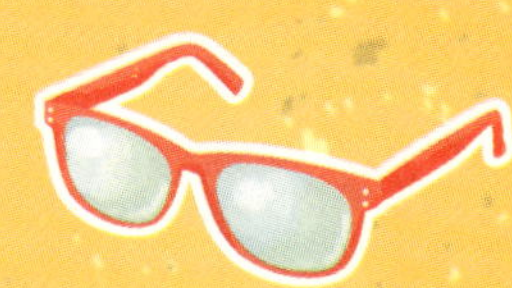

EYE GLASSES

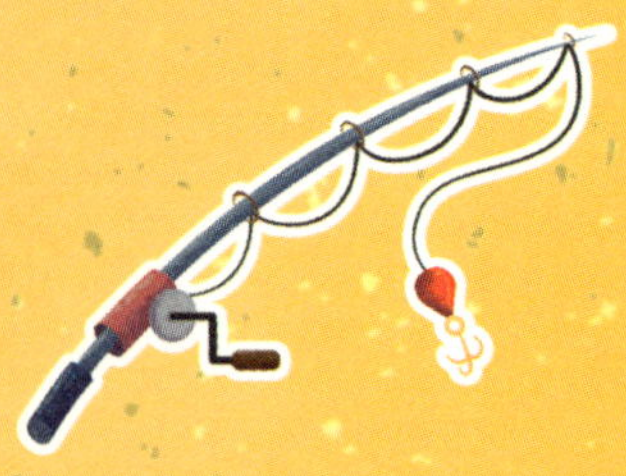

FISHING ROD

FRAME

FLOAT

FRIES

FURNITURE

FROG

LET'S PRACTICE TO TRACE LETTER F AND RECOGNISE THESE ASSOCIATED OBJECTS.

NOW, IT'S TIME TO TRACE LETTER F ON THE FOUR LINES.

BRAVO! NOW ONLY FOLLOW THE SMART DOTS TO WRITE THE LETTER F.

FOSSILS

FENCE

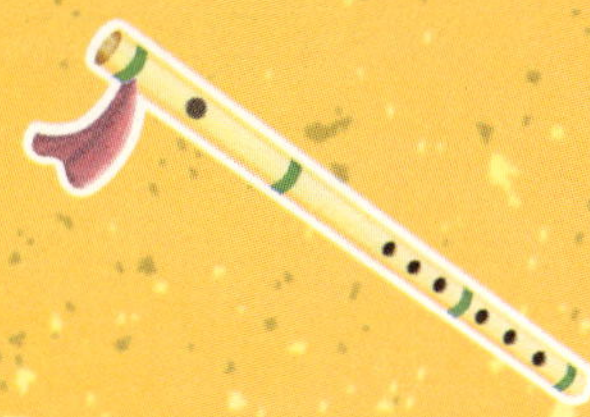

FLUTE

FINGERS

FIREFIGHTER

FONDUE

HALLOWEEN

HAIR DRYER

HAMSTER

HAMBURGER

HEDGEHOG

HIVE

LET'S PRACTICE TO TRACE LETTER H AND RECOGNISE THESE ASSOCIATED OBJECTS.

NOW, IT'S TIME TO TRACE LETTER H ON THE FOUR LINES.

BRAVO! NOW ONLY FOLLOW THE SMART DOTS TO WRITE THE LETTER H.

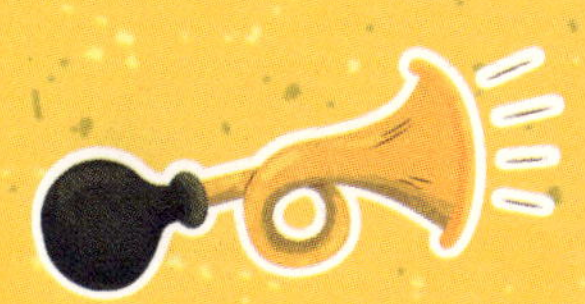

HORN

HOTDOG

HERMIT CRAB

HAIRBAND

HOUSEBOAT

HIBISCUS

KIWI

KENNEL

KITTEN

KEYBOARD

KERNELS

KIMONO

LET'S PRACTICE TO TRACE LETTER K AND RECOGNISE THESE ASSOCIATED OBJECTS.

NOW, IT'S TIME TO TRACE LETTER K ON THE FOUR LINES.

BRAVO! NOW ONLY FOLLOW THE SMART DOTS TO WRITE THE LETTER K.

KALE

KALEIDOSCOPE

KINGFISHER

KEYCHAIN

KARATE

KITE

AQUARIUM

ASTRONAUT

ANGEL

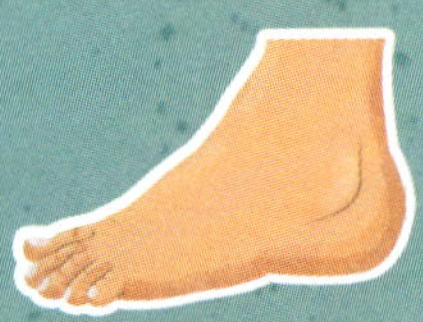

ANKLE

ALMOND

APRON

LET'S PRACTICE TO TRACE LETTER A AND RECOGNISE THESE ASSOCIATED OBJECTS.

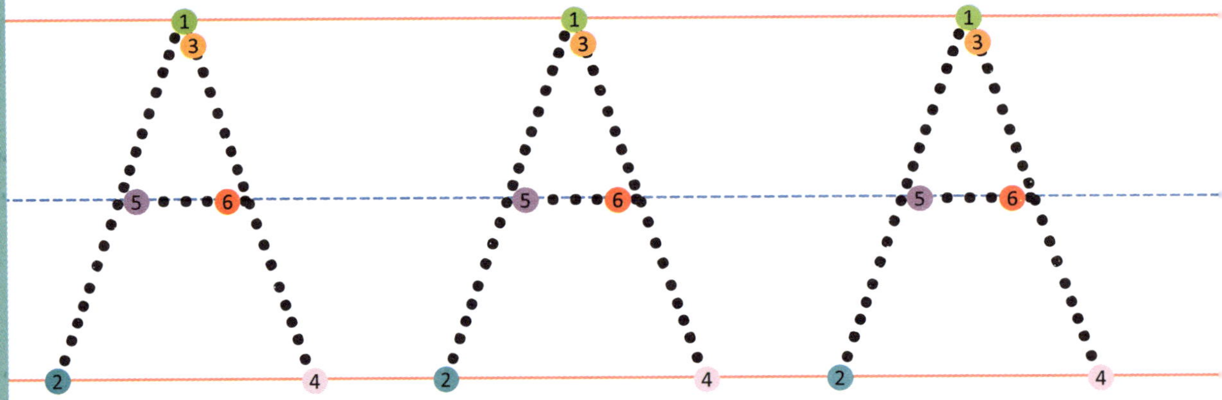

NOW, IT'S TIME TO TRACE LETTER A ON THE FOUR LINES.

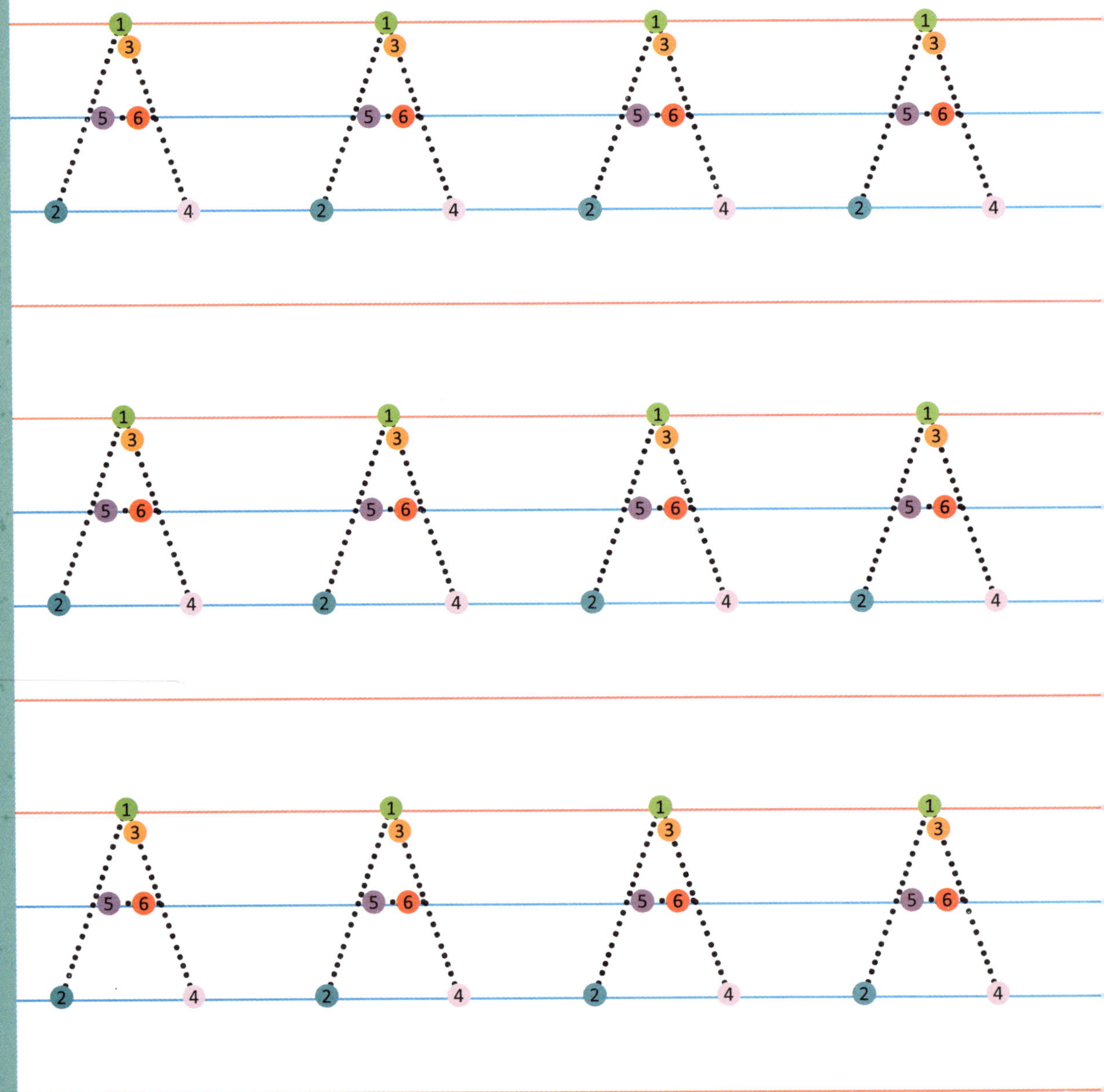

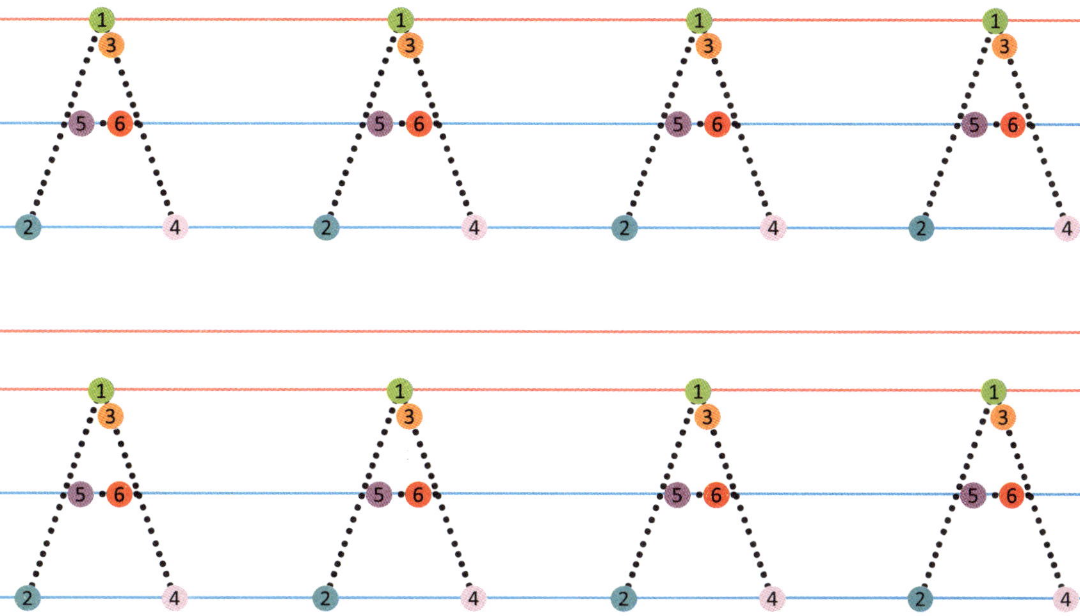

BRAVO! NOW ONLY FOLLOW THE SMART DOTS TO WRITE THE LETTER A.

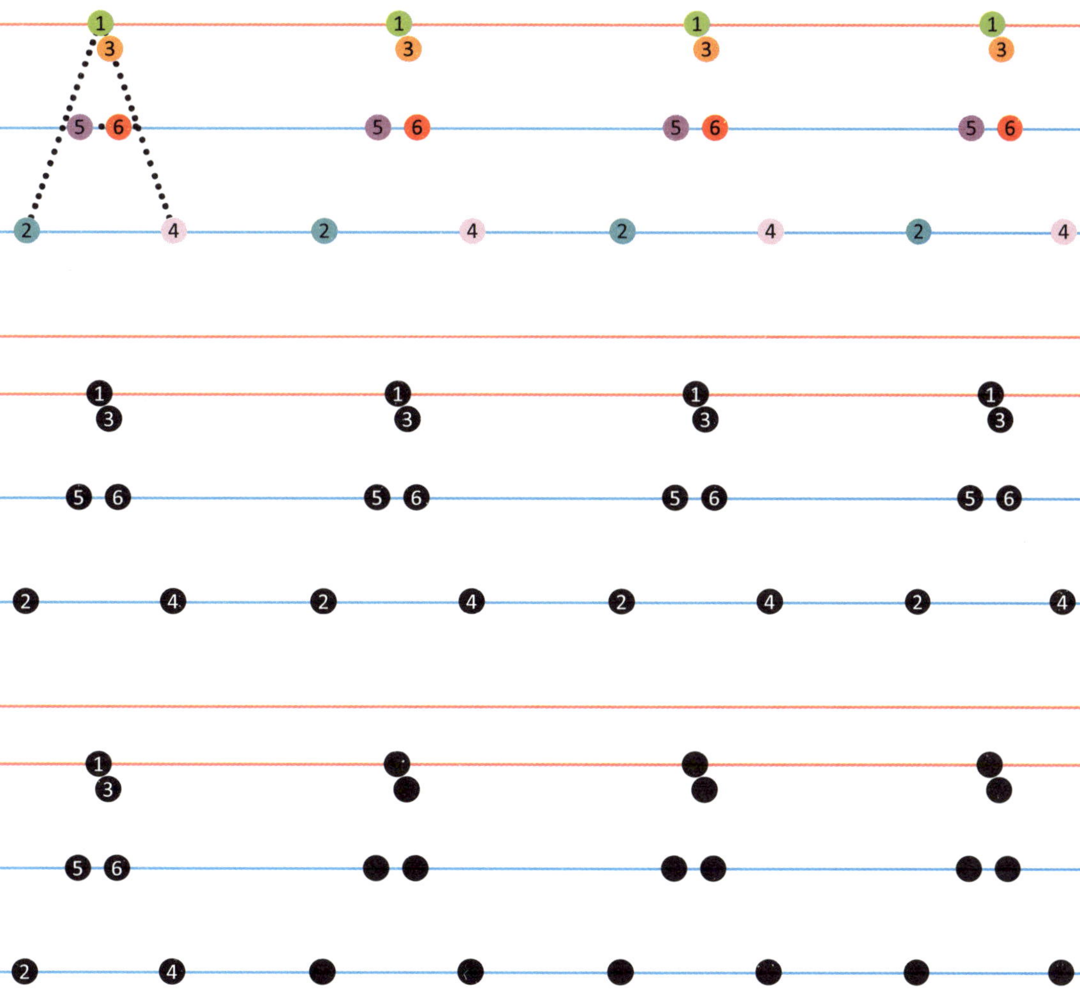

AWARD

ANTARCTICA

ASIA

ALIEN

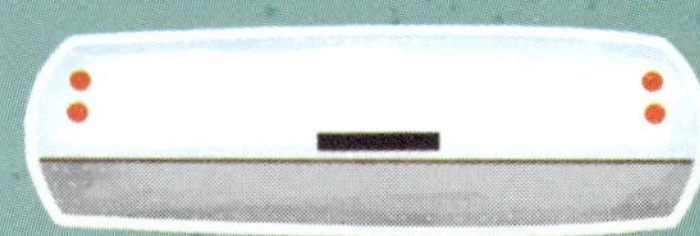

AIR CONDITIONER

AFRICA

VENUS

VIKING

VITAMINS

VACCUM CLEANER

VINE

VACCINE

LET'S PRACTICE TO TRACE LETTER V AND RECOGNISE THESE ASSOCIATED OBJECTS.

NOW, IT'S TIME TO TRACE LETTER V ON THE FOUR LINES.

BRAVO! NOW ONLY FOLLOW THE SMART DOTS TO WRITE THE LETTER V.

VIOLET

VAMPIRE

VIETNAM

VIPER SNAKE

VIDEO CAMERA

VINEGAR

WAND

WASHING MACHINE

WHEELCHAIR

WALLET

WHITE SHARK

WASP

LET'S PRACTICE TO TRACE LETTER W AND RECOGNISE THESE ASSOCIATED OBJECTS.

NOW, IT'S TIME TO TRACE LETTER W ON THE FOUR LINES.

WOODPECKER

WOOL

BRAVO! NOW ONLY FOLLOW THE SMART DOTS TO WRITE THE LETTER W.

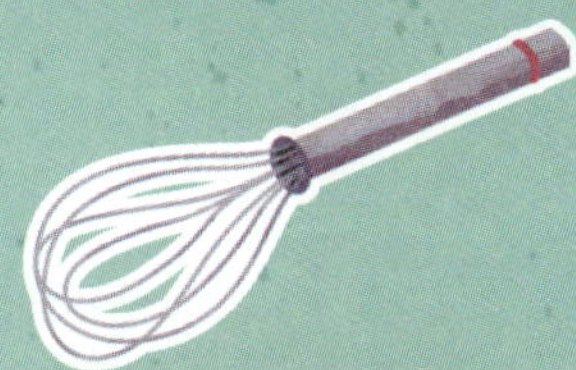

WHISK

WALL

WHEAT

WEB

LET'S PRACTICE TO TRACE LETTER X AND RECOGNISE THESE ASSOCIATED OBJECTS.

NOW, IT'S TIME TO TRACE LETTER X ON THE FOUR LINES.

XYLOPHONE

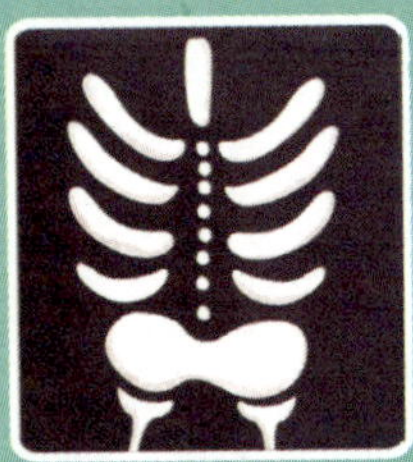
X-RAY

X-RAY FISH

X-MAS TREE

XEROX MACHINE

XERUS

BRAVO! NOW ONLY FOLLOW THE SMART DOTS TO WRITE THE THE LETTER X.

YAM

YELLOW

YOGURT

YAK

YOLK

YARN

LET'S PRACTICE TO TRACE LETTER Y AND RECOGNISE THESE ASSOCIATED OBJECTS.

NOW, IT'S TIME TO TRACE LETTER Y ON THE FOUR LINES.

BRAVO! NOW ONLY FOLLOW THE SMART DOTS TO WRITE THE LETTER Y.

MUFFIN

MITTENS

MERMAID

MARS

MOSQUITO

MARIGOLD

LET'S PRACTICE TO TRACE LETTER M AND RECOGNISE THESE ASSOCIATED OBJECTS.

NOW, IT'S TIME TO TRACE LETTER M ON THE FOUR LINES.

BRAVO! NOW ONLY FOLLOW THE SMART DOTS TO WRITE THE LETTER M.

MOOSE

MARBLES

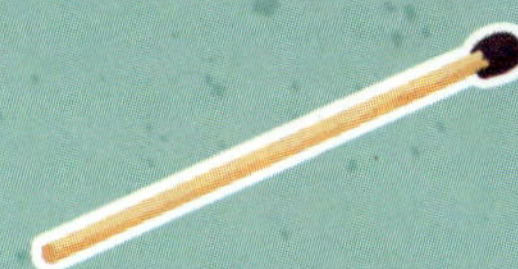

MATCHSTICK

MASK

MEXICO

MEDAL

NARWHAL WHALE

NACHOS

NURSE

NEPTUNE

NIGHTINGALE

NINJA

LET'S PRACTICE TO TRACE LETTER N AND RECOGNISE THESE ASSOCIATED OBJECTS.

NOW, IT'S TIME TO TRACE LETTER N ON THE FOUR LINES.

BRAVO! NOW ONLY FOLLOW THE SMART DOTS TO WRITE THE LETTER N.

NAILCUTTER

NORTH AMERICA

NOTE

NUMBER

NEBULIZER

NUTMEG

LET'S PRACTICE TO TRACE LETTER Z AND RECOGNISE THESE ASSOCIATED OBJECTS.

NOW, IT'S TIME TO TRACE LETTER Z ON THE FOUR LINES.

ZOO

ZIG-ZAG

ZIPLOCK BAG

ZIP

ZEBRA CROSSING

ZEBRA

BRAVO! NOW ONLY FOLLOW THE SMART DOTS TO WRITE THE LETTER Z.

ZEBRA SHARK

ZIP LINE

ZOMBIE

ZUCCHINI

ZERO

ZEPPELIN

CAMEL

COAT

CASTLE

CARROT

CACTUS

CALF

LET'S PRACTICE TO TRACE LETTER C AND RECOGNISE THESE ASSOCIATED OBJECTS.

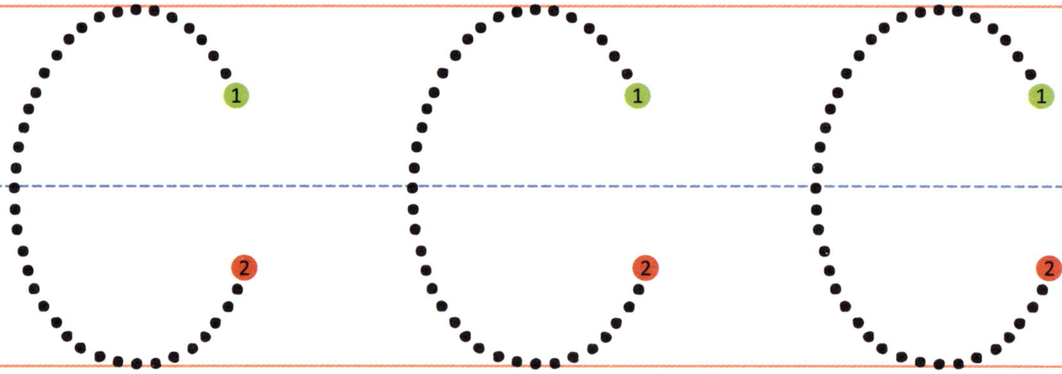

NOW, IT'S TIME TO TRACE LETTER C ON THE FOUR LINES.

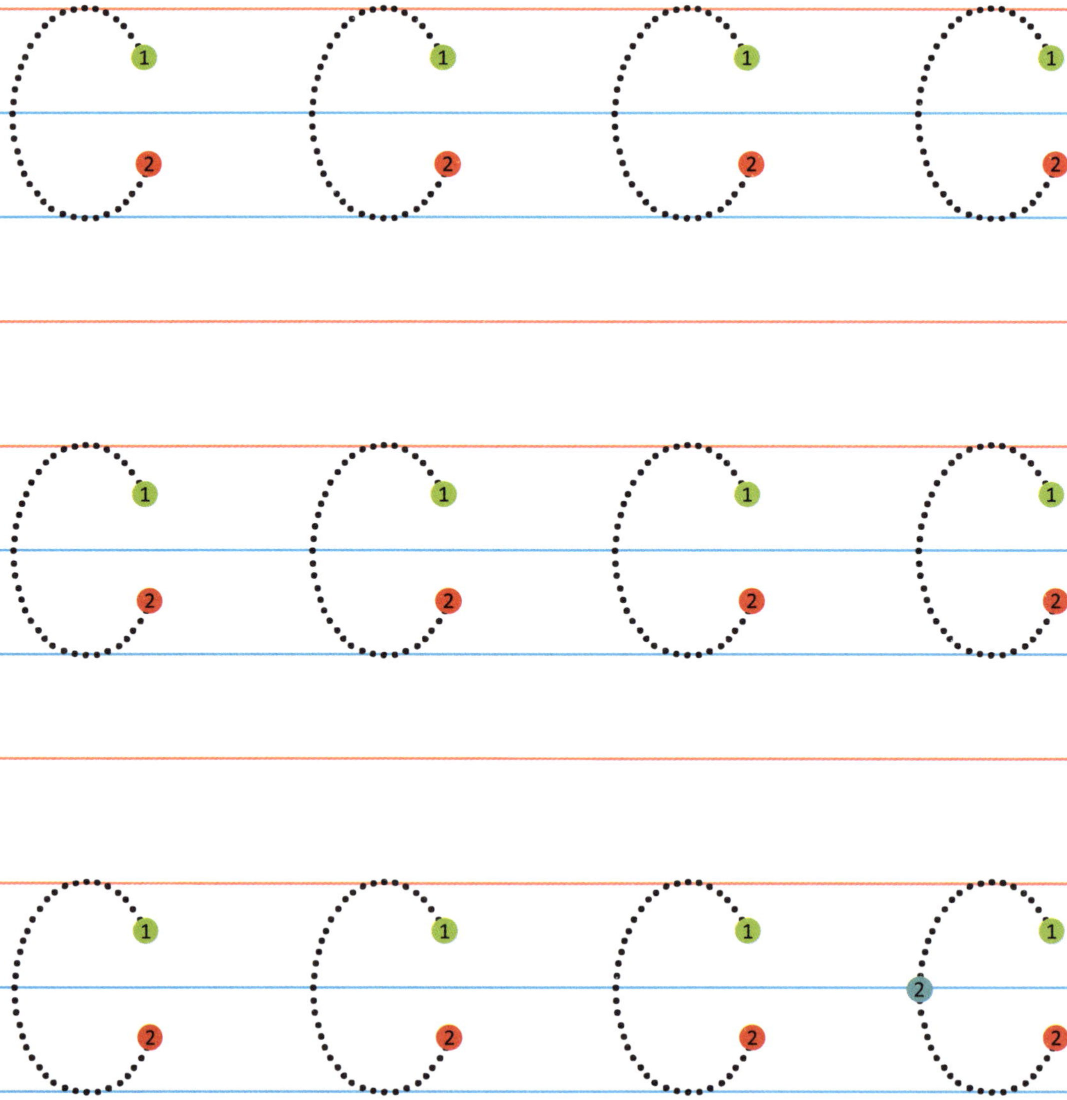

BRAVO! NOW ONLY FOLLOW THE SMART DOTS TO WRITE THE LETTER C.

CALENDAR

CARPENTER

CASH

COTTAGE

COMPUTER

COMB

OATMEAL

ORCHID

OLIVE

OTTER

OAK TREE

OCEANIA

LET'S PRACTICE TO TRACE LETTER O AND RECOGNISE THESE ASSOCIATED OBJECTS.

NOW, IT'S TIME TO TRACE LETTER O ON THE FOUR LINES.

BRAVO! NOW ONLY FOLLOW THE SMART DOTS TO WRITE THE LETTER O.

OKRA

OBSERVATORY

OFFICE

OVERCOAT

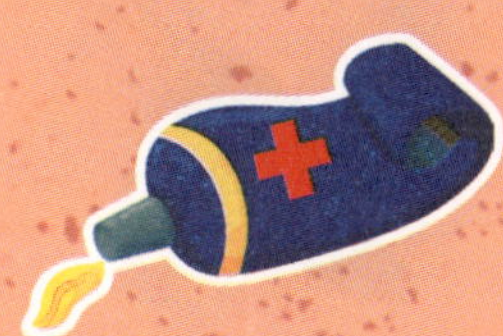
OINTMENT

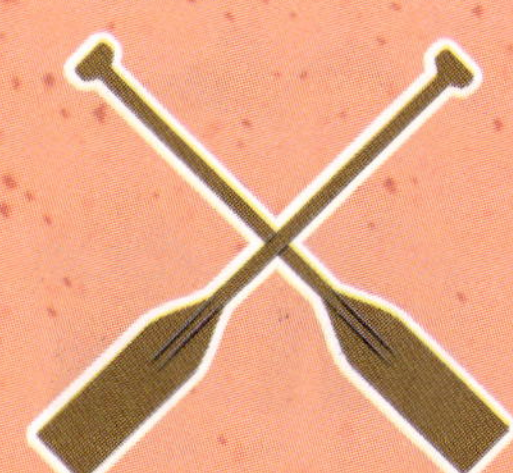
OAR

QUEEN

QUILT

QUILL

QUESTION MARK

QUAIL

QUEUE

LET'S PRACTICE TO TRACE LETTER Q AND RECOGNISE THESE ASSOCIATED OBJECTS.

NOW, IT'S TIME TO TRACE LETTER Q ON THE FOUR LINES.

BRAVO! NOW ONLY FOLLOW THE SMART DOTS TO WRITE THE LETTER Q.

QUINOA

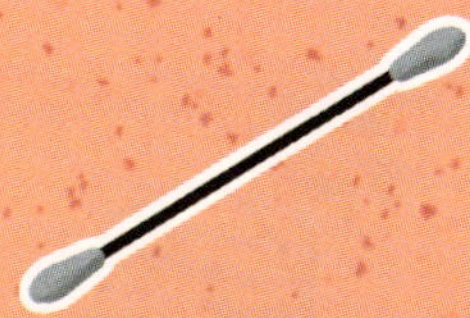

Q-TIP

QUIET

QUOTE

QATAR

QUIZ

PANTHER

PANSY

PEACOCK

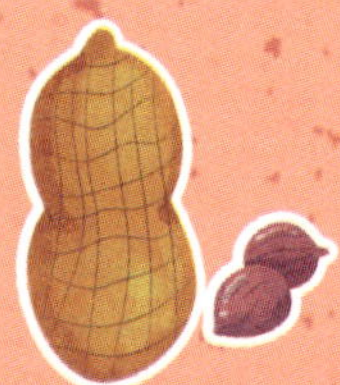

PEANUT

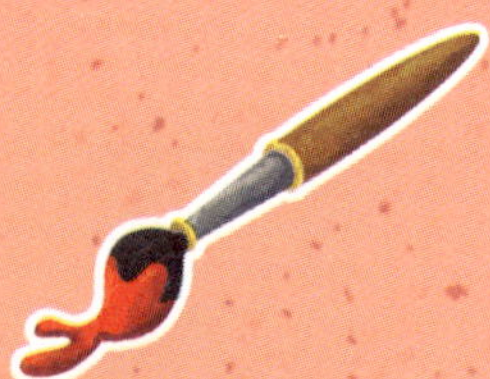

PAINTBRUSH

PIANO

LET'S PRACTICE TO TRACE LETTER P AND RECOGNISE THESE ASSOCIATED OBJECTS.

NOW, IT'S TIME TO TRACE LETTER P ON THE FOUR LINES.

BRAVO! NOW ONLY FOLLOW THE SMART DOTS TO WRITE THE LETTER P.

POTATO

PLANETS

POPCORN

POLICEMAN

PHOTOGRAPH

PIRATE

RAINCOAT

ROOSTER

RUG

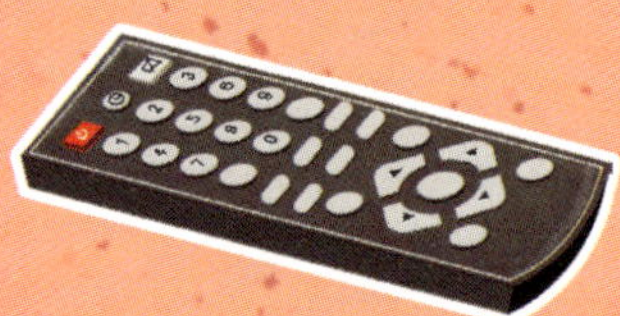

REMOTE

REINDEER

ROCK

LET'S PRACTICE TO TRACE LETTER R AND RECOGNISE THESE ASSOCIATED OBJECTS.

NOW, IT'S TIME TO TRACE LETTER R ON THE FOUR LINES.

BRAVO! NOW ONLY FOLLOW THE SMART DOTS TO WRITE THE LETTER R.

RIVER

RASPBERRY

ROLLERCOASTER

RUSSIA

ROSEMARY

RACE

DRESS

DIAPER

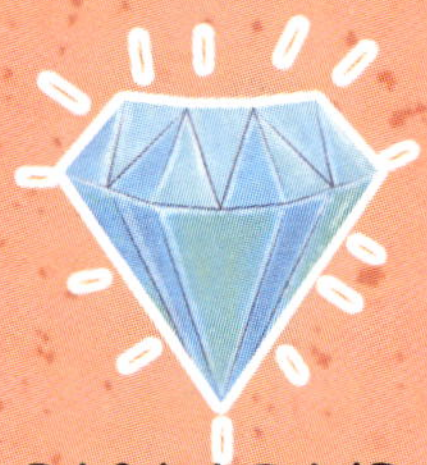

DIAMOND

DONKEY

DRAGONFLY

DAISY

LET'S PRACTICE TO TRACE LETTER D AND RECOGNISE THESE ASSOCIATED OBJECTS.

NOW, IT'S TIME TO TRACE LETTER D ON THE FOUR LINES.

BRAVO! NOW ONLY FOLLOW THE SMART DOTS TO WRITE THE LETTER D.

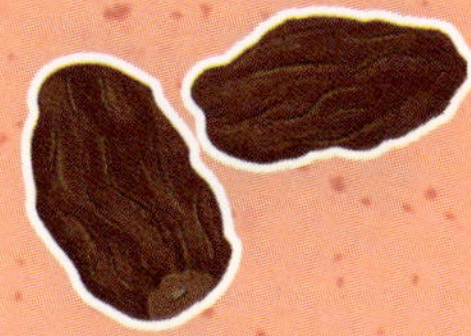
DATE

DENIM

DAGGER

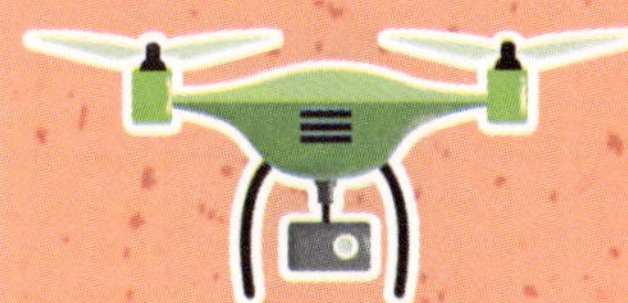
DRONE

DAFFODIL

DRIVER

BALLOON

BENCH

BATTERY

BOWL

BROCCOLI

BEETLE

LET'S PRACTICE TO TRACE LETTER B AND RECOGNISE THESE ASSOCIATED OBJECTS.

NOW, IT'S TIME TO TRACE LETTER B ON THE FOUR LINES.

BRAVO! NOW ONLY FOLLOW THE SMART DOTS TO WRITE THE LETTER B.

BEAR

BUCKET

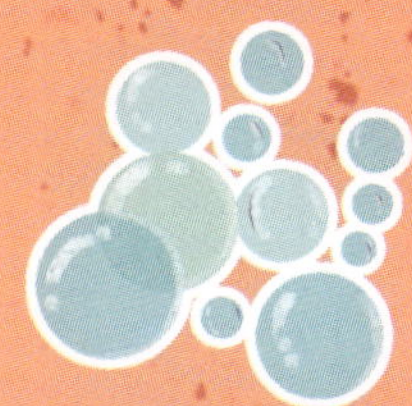

BUBBLES

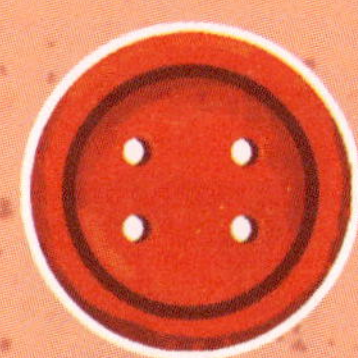

BUTTON

BAMBOO

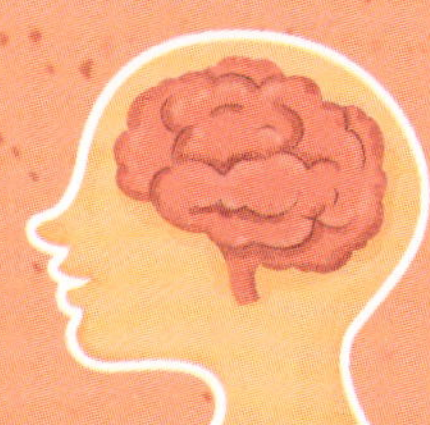

BRAIN

JERSEY

JIG-SAW

JUPITER

JACKAL

JESTER

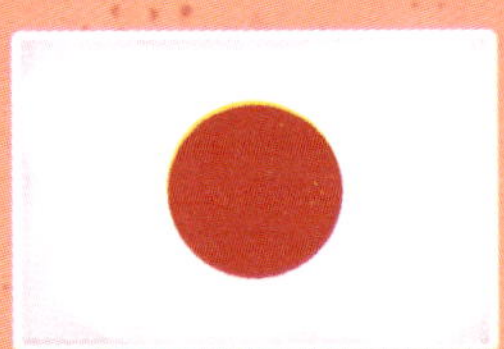

JAPAN

LET'S PRACTICE TO TRACE LETTER J AND RECOGNISE THESE ASSOCIATED OBJECTS.

NOW, IT'S TIME TO TRACE LETTER J ON THE FOUR LINES.

BRAVO! NOW ONLY FOLLOW THE SMART DOTS TO WRITE THE LETTER J.

JASMINE

JAY

JUMPSUIT

JEWELLERY

JEEP

JACKET

UMBRELLA

UP

UNIFORM

UNICORN

UNDER GARMENTS

URN

LET'S PRACTICE TO TRACE LETTER U AND RECOGNISE THESE ASSOCIATED OBJECTS.

NOW, IT'S TIME TO TRACE LETTER U ON THE FOUR LINES.

BRAVO! NOW ONLY FOLLOW THE SMART DOTS TO WRITE THE LETTER U.

UTENSILS

U-TURN

URANUS

UMPIRE

UNITED STATES OF AMERICA

USB DRIVE

LET'S PRACTICE TO TRACE LETTER S AND RECOGNISE THESE ASSOCIATED OBJECTS.

NOW, IT'S TIME TO TRACE LETTER S ON THE FOUR LINES.

SPIDER

STORK

SANDWICH

SNOWMAN

SANDALS

SNAIL

BRAVO! NOW ONLY FOLLOW THE SMART DOTS TO WRITE THE LETTER S.

SAXOPHONE

SOUTH AMERICA

SOLDIER

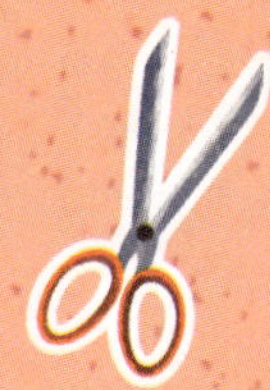

SCISSORS

SINGAPORE

SCARF

GEMSTONE

GOOSE

GUAVA

GLOVES

GOLD

GOLF

LET'S PRACTICE TO TRACE LETTER G AND RECOGNISE THESE ASSOCIATED OBJECTS.

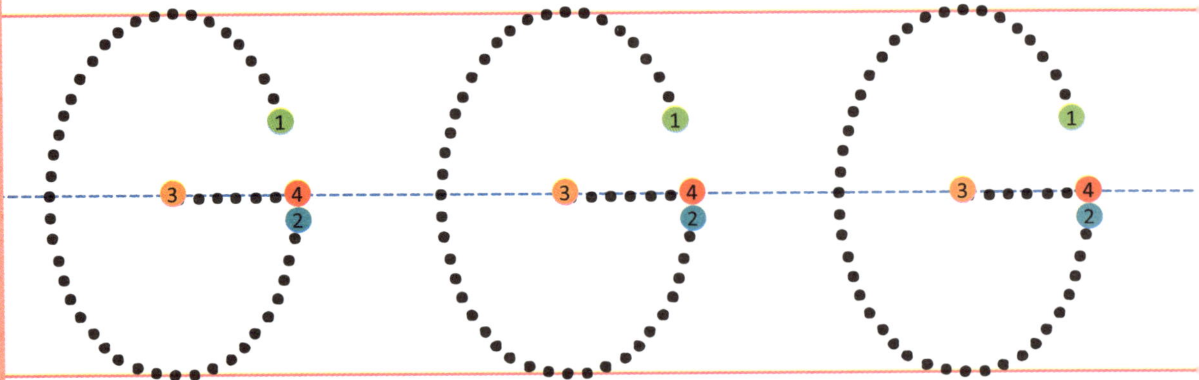

NOW, IT'S TIME TO TRACE LETTER G ON THE FOUR LINES.

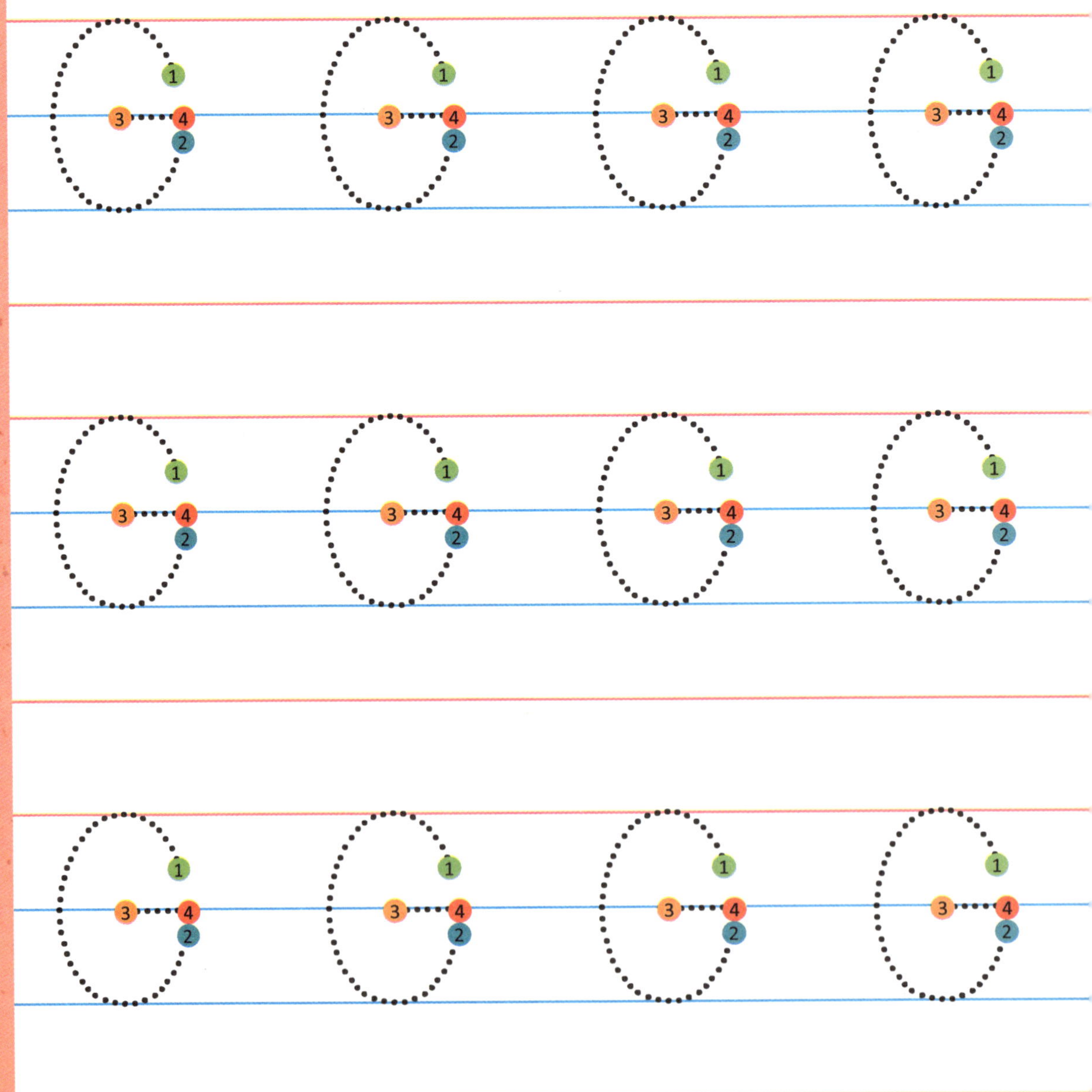

BRAVO! NOW ONLY FOLLOW THE SMART DOTS TO WRITE THE LETTER G.

GARLAND

GINGERBREAD

GHOST

GRASSHOPPER

GERMANY

GARLIC

Lil Legends

Certificate of

Achievement

This is to certify that .... has successfully completed the **Uppercase Tracing & Vocabulary Book.** He/She has also completed Level-2 of our Pre-writing Program.

OSWAAL BOOKS®
LEARNING MADE SIMPLE